Ladybird
HOMEWORK HELPERS
Adding Up
Sticker Book

Written by Amanda Archer

Illustrated by Ian Cunliffe

Educational Consultant: Geraldine Taylor

Party puzzlers

All adding up starts with good counting skills.

Count the candles

How many candles can you count on these birthday cakes?
Write the number next to each one. This number is the **total**.

5

5 candles

candles

candles

Use the candle stickers to decorate this cake. How many are there? Write in the total.

candles

How many children are at my party? I've made an ice cream for each one.

There are [ ] children at your party.

Fun with one

Count the objects below, then add one more
to each from the sticker sheet.
Write the correct numbers in the boxes.

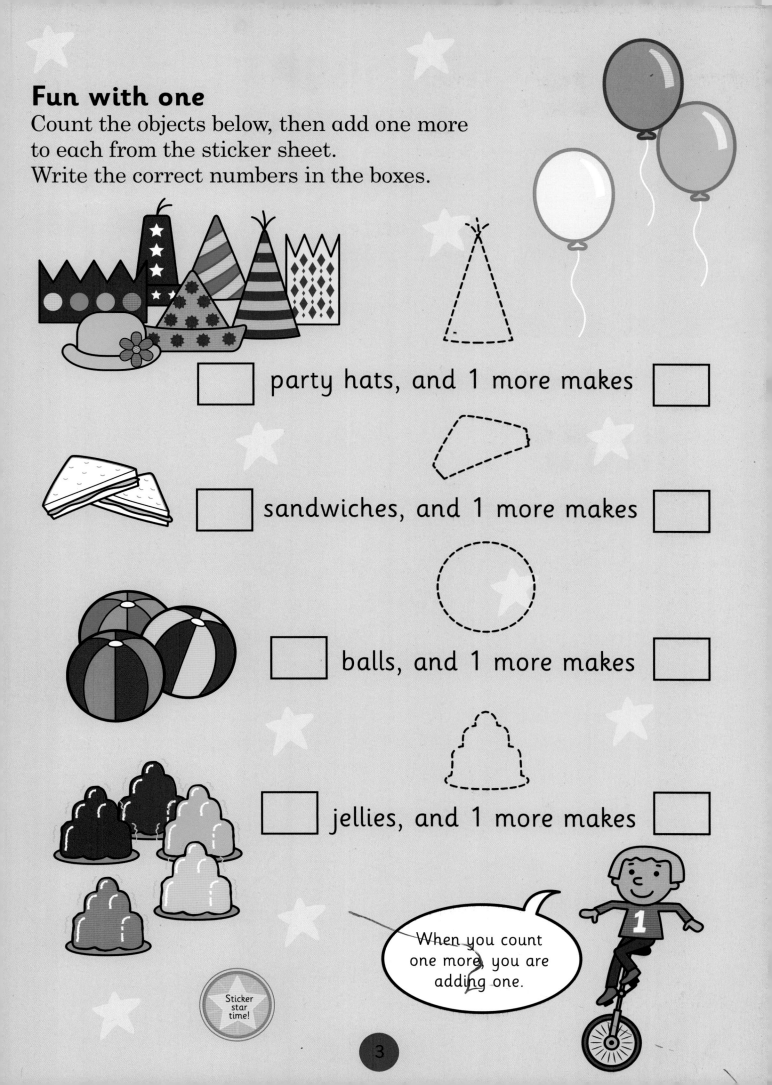

[ ] party hats, and 1 more makes [ ]

[ ] sandwiches, and 1 more makes [ ]

[ ] balls, and 1 more makes [ ]

[ ] jellies, and 1 more makes [ ]

Sticker star time!

When you count one more, you are adding one.

3

Sums at the shops

Sometimes when we are counting on, we need to add **two more** things to the total.

Two for tea

The twins are coming for tea so you need to buy two more of everything.

Write the new totals below.

add 2 more to make ☐

add 2 more to make ☐

add 2 more to make ☐

add 2 more to make ☐

Plus 2 practice

Look at each of the sums below then write in the correct answer.

2 + 7 = ☐   6 + 2 = ☐   8 + 2 = ☐

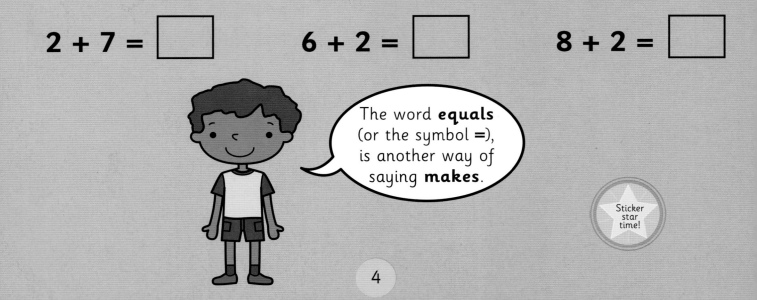

The word **equals** (or the symbol **=**), is another way of saying **makes**.

Sticker star time!

Some more sums

Can you work out the answers to these sums?
Put the correct answer stickers in place.

You can use the **+** symbol or the word **plus** to show that you are adding.

9 + 2 =

4 + 2 =

2 + 5 =

Zero zone

Now you can't carry another thing! What happens if you add zero more items to your shopping bags? Write in the answers.

+ 0 =

+ 0 =

+ 0 =

Zero is another word for **none**.

To ten and beyond

Ten pin teaser

There are lots of sums at the bowling alley.
Look at the questions below and write the answers in the boxes.

add = ☐

add = ☐

add = ☐

add = ☐

If I knock down 5 pins with my first throw, how many do I need to knock down with my next throw to score a perfect 10?

☐

6

Spot the spots

A game of dominoes can help us to practise adding up to 12. Count the spots on each section of the dominoes and write the numbers in the boxes.

Now stick in the correct total for each domino.

Can you find two more picture stickers that feature the number 12?

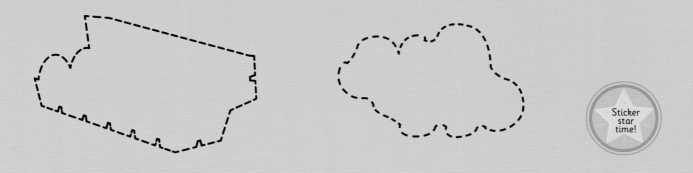

Sticker star time!

7

Maths chatter

There are many different words that tell us when it is time to use addition.

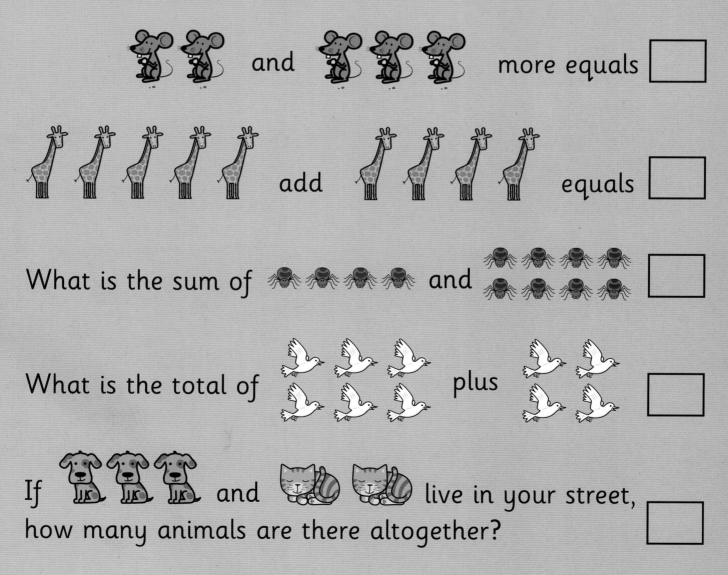

more

plus

altogether

and

add

total

sum

Animal antics

Write in the answers to the animal sums below.

and   more equals ☐

add   equals ☐

What is the sum of   and   ☐

What is the total of   plus   ☐

If   and   live in your street, how many animals are there altogether? ☐

All the right answers

Different combinations of numbers can add up to the same total.

Nibbling numbers
Look at the sums in the air bubbles, then stick in the right answer fish.

7 + 2

6 + 9

1 + 10

6 + 3

2 + 13

8 + 3

8 + 1

8 + 7

5 + 6

7 + 8

2 + 9

5 + 4

Sticker star time!

Up and down the line

A **number line** can help us with adding up.

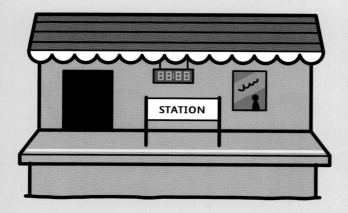

Put your finger on the bigger number in the sum and then count on the smaller number. When you finish counting, you have your answer.

Write the answers to the sums below in the boxes. Use the number line to help you if you need to.

16 + 5 = 21   4 + 4 = 8

8 + 8 = 16   13 + 7 = 7

14 + 5 = 19

3 + 9 = 10

A faster way of moving along the number line is to count in bigger steps, such as 2s and 5s.

10 11

10

Train-track maths

Now try these sums. Write the answers in the boxes. When you have finished, stick the train stickers next to the track.

9 + 4 = 13   2 + 13 = 13

10 + 8 = 18   15 + 4 = 19

| 12 | 13 | 14 | 15 | 16 | 17 | 18 | 19 | 20 | 21 | 22 | | 2 |

Playing with numbers

Adding up can help us learn how numbers work.
A whole number like 10 is made up of parts.
If you know the parts you can put them together
again to make a whole.

4 + = 10

Perfect pairs

Find a partner for
each child. Each number
pair must add up to 10.

7 + = 10

6 + = 10

All these perfect pairs
are called **number
pairs**. They all add up
to the same total.

5 + 5 = 10

Super sets

Split this set of 20 footballs into two parts by drawing a circle around some of them. Now count up how many are in each section.

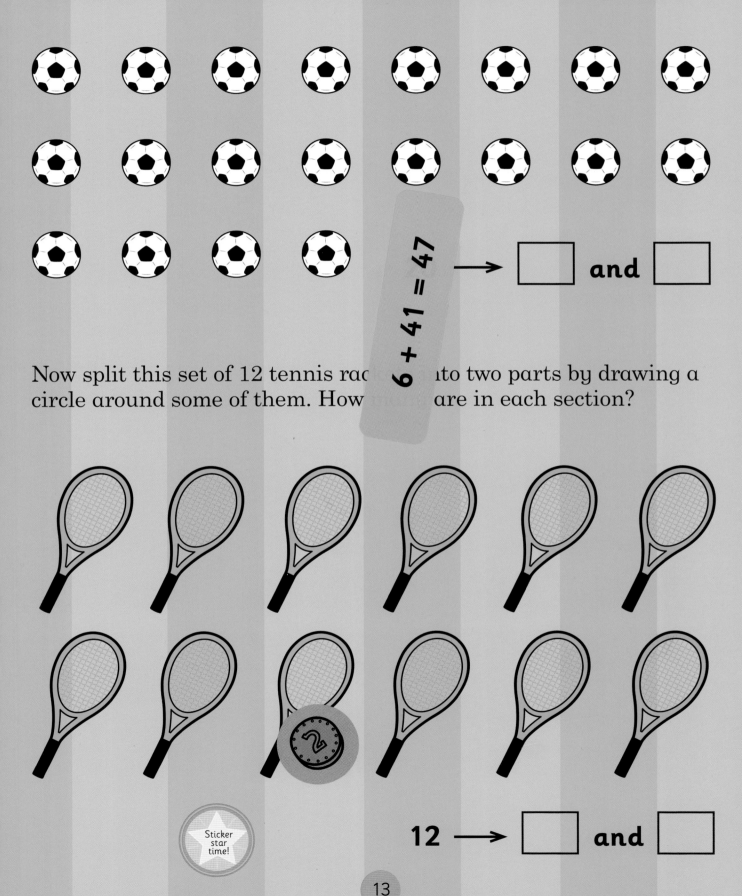

$6 + 41 = 47$

→ ☐ and ☐

Now split this set of 12 tennis rackets into two parts by drawing a circle around some of them. How many are in each section?

12 → ☐ and ☐

Sticker star time!

13

Swap shop

Now let's try adding three numbers together.

Top toys

Work out the answers to the sums below, then follow the lines to see if you are right.

$20 + 7 + 3 = 30$

$6 + 3 + 3 = 12$

$2 + 3 + 4 = 9$

30

12

9

Adding more and more

Jungle hide and seek

Can you see the creatures in the trees? Work out the sums to find out how many animals are hiding and write your answers in the boxes.

$5 + 10 + 12 =$ 12

$7 + 7 + 7 + 8 =$ 1P

$1 + 3 + 4 + 1 =$ P

$9 + 11 + 3 =$ 30

$10 + 13 + 17 =$

$3 + 4 + 2 + 6 =$ 15

Sticker star time!

The sky's the limit!

Some addition problems have numbers missing. We need to use the numbers we have to work out what is missing.

Cloud cover

Fill in the blanks in these problems. Take the first number away from the answer to work out what the missing number is.

For example: $12 + \boxed{} = 35$

($35 - 12 = 23$, so 23 is the number that goes in the box.)

When you finish each one, put the right picture sticker in front of the clouds.

$15 + \boxed{} = 40$

$10 + \boxed{} = 19$

$\boxed{} + 4 = 12$

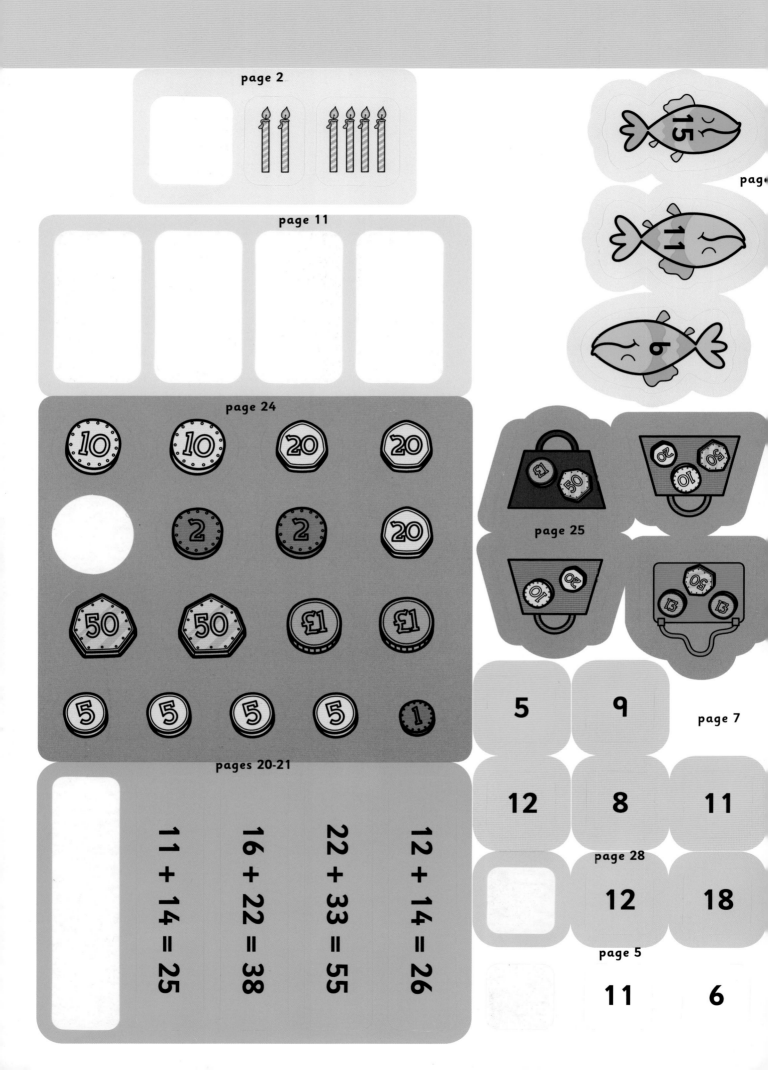

page 2

page 11

page 24

pages 20-21

11 + 14 = 25

16 + 22 = 38

22 + 33 = 55

12 + 14 = 26

page 25

page 7

5

9

12

8

11

page 28

12

18

page 5

11

6

pages 16-17

page 26

page 23

page 7

pages 16-17

page 12

page 3

page 12

$4 + \boxed{} = 29$

$14 + \boxed{} = 36$

$13 + \boxed{} = 26$

These types of sums are called **equations**.

Daft doublers

These crazy aliens only travel in equal numbers!
Double up each type, then write in the totals.

 $+$  $= \boxed{}$

$+ \quad = \boxed{}$

Sticker star time!

17

Challenging times

Some addition sums are set out differently and you have to work out the answer in a different way.

Message in a bottle

Tom Smythe has been stranded on this island for weeks! Read his letter, then write in the correct answers to the questions.

To whoever may find this letter,

Time has passed so slowly on this island, I can't remember when I got here! I made a list of the days:

Warm sunny days   17
Blistering hot days   12
Wet days   24

I often stare out at the ocean, hoping to be saved. Once I saw 3 pirate ships, but they sailed away.

If you find this letter please send help. Only the animals keep me cheerful. I've spotted two whales, and a dozen crabs have tiptoed past me on the sand. I've even seen an octopus waggling his tentacles.

Yours hopefully,

Tom Smythe.

How many days has Tom been on the island in total?

On how many days was there rain?

How many ships have sailed past the island?

Count up all of the animals that Tom has spotted.

Sticker star time!

Bigger and bigger!

You can follow the same rules for adding, no matter how big the numbers get.

Even large two-digit sums are easy when you know how.

Market day

Farmer Brown is counting up the animals he needs to take to the market. Find the correct sticker sums to go with the signs he's put up around the farm.

26 HORSES

55 CHICKENS

38 GEESE

1 2 3 4 5 6 7 8 9 10 11 12 13 14 15 16 17 18 19 20 21 22 23 24 25

47 COWS

25 PIGS

Counting sheep
Help Farmer Brown count his sheep.
Write your answers in the boxes.

Use a number line to help you count forward to the right answer.

12 + 19 = ☐ lambs

28 + 14 = ☐ ewes

15 + 27 = ☐ rams

Sticker star time!

26 27 28 29 30 31 32 33 34 35 36 37 38 39 40 41 42 43 44 45 46 47 48 49 50

Plus is no fuss

When you are adding large numbers together, try adding the parts separately. This is called **partitioning**.

For example, if you are adding 35 and 27, you can split the numbers up like this:

$(30 + 5) + (20 + 7) = (30 + 20) + (5 + 7) = 50 + 12 = 62$

Work out the sums below. Use another piece of paper for your working out if you need to.

35 + 7 = ⬜

26 + 24 = ⬜

19 + 17 = ⬜

34 + 12 = ⬜

1 2 3 4 5 6 7 8 9 10 11 12 13 14 15 16 17 18 19 20 21 22 23 24 25

Number grids

Complete the number grids below.
Stick in a honey pot for every one you finish.

Make each line add up to 18.

3			1	8
2				
		4		3

Make each line add up to 25.

5			4	
				5
8	7			1

Try different numbers to see if they work and change them if you need to. Use a piece of paper to jot down your workings.

Sticker star time!

26 27 28 29 30 31 32 33 34 35 36 37 38 39 40 41 42 43 44 45 46 47 48 49 50

23

Funny money

Food festival!

The children are off to the school food festival. Can you help them work out how much money they need to buy some snacks?

Find the sticker coins to make the exact money to buy each treat.

apple
15p

pizza
55p

juice
18p

spaghetti
£2.45

potato
74p

Put the correct bag sticker next to each child.

Sticker star time!

I've got £2.50.

I've got 80p.

I've got 30p.

I've got £1.50.

When you are working out how to pay for something, it is easier to use as few coins as possible.

25

Undersea adding game

START
Count up to 10 and back down again without making a mistake.

Play this adding game with up to three friends.

Press the four coloured shell stickers onto some card and then carefully cut them out.
Choose a counter each then find a die to get started.

How to play
Take turns to throw the die, then move forward along the board.

Each of the blue squares has a special challenge. If your fellow voyagers agree that it has been completed successfully, that player may move forward **1 extra square**.

The winner is the first player to get to the desert island!

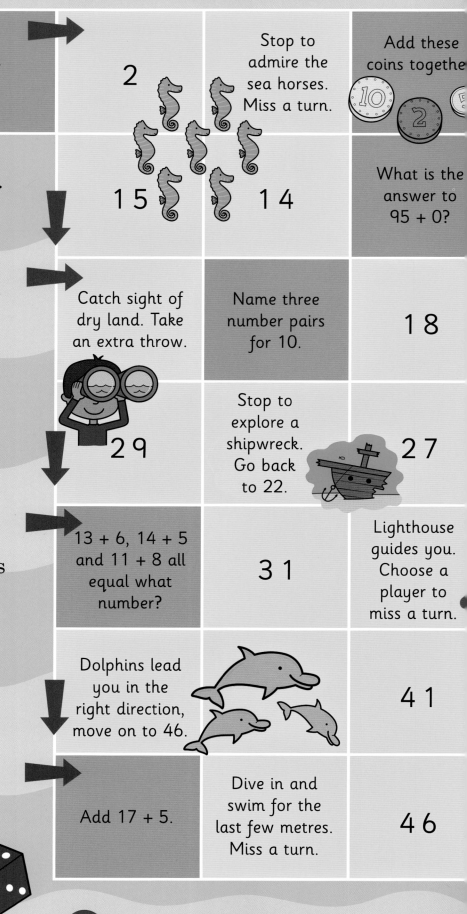

2

Stop to admire the sea horses. Miss a turn.

Add these coins together

15   14

What is the answer to 95 + 0?

Catch sight of dry land. Take an extra throw.

Name three number pairs for 10.

18

29

Stop to explore a shipwreck. Go back to 22.

27

13 + 6, 14 + 5 and 11 + 8 all equal what number?

31

Lighthouse guides you. Choose a player to miss a turn.

Dolphins lead you in the right direction, move on to 46.

41

Add 17 + 5.

Dive in and swim for the last few metres. Miss a turn.

46

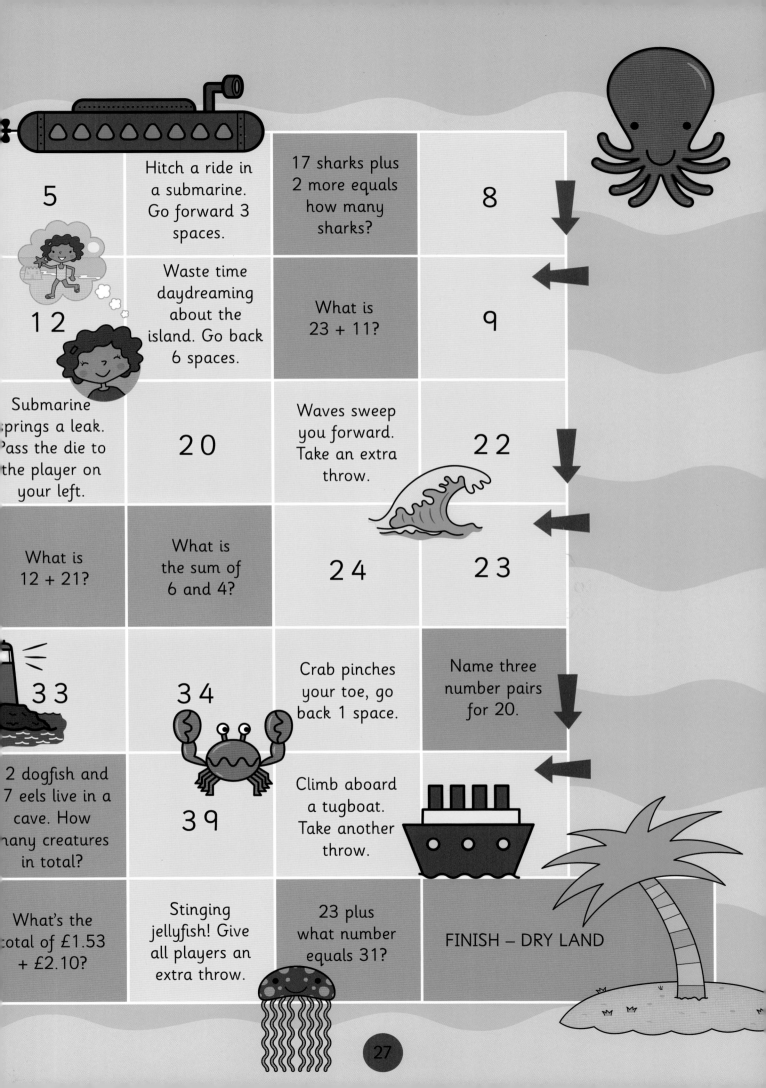

5

Hitch a ride in a submarine. Go forward 3 spaces.

17 sharks plus 2 more equals how many sharks?

8

12

Waste time daydreaming about the island. Go back 6 spaces.

What is 23 + 11?

9

Submarine springs a leak. Pass the die to the player on your left.

20

Waves sweep you forward. Take an extra throw.

22

What is 12 + 21?

What is the sum of 6 and 4?

24

23

33

34

Crab pinches your toe, go back 1 space.

Name three number pairs for 20.

2 dogfish and 7 eels live in a cave. How many creatures in total?

39

Climb aboard a tugboat. Take another throw.

What's the total of £1.53 + £2.10?

Stinging jellyfish! Give all players an extra throw.

23 plus what number equals 31?

FINISH — DRY LAND

Amazing adders quiz

Chocolate challenge
Count up the chocolate chunks then add them together to solve each of the sums.

$+$ $=$ ☐

$+$ $=$ ☐

$+$ $=$ ☐

Pirate problems
Stick in the correct answers before the friendly smile disappears from Old Blackbeard's face.

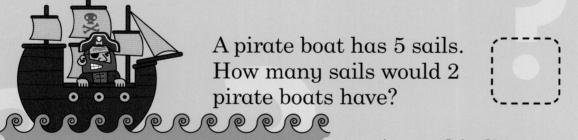

A pirate boat has 5 sails. How many sails would 2 pirate boats have?

A warship has 4 cannons. How many cannons would 3 warships have in total?

Captain Bluebeard has 4 gold coins, Pirate Pete has 6 coins and Davey Morgan has 8 coins. How many coins do they have altogether?

Eight is great

The answer to each of these sums is 88.
Fill in the blanks to solve the equations below.

14 + ☐ = 88   53 + ☐ = 88

☐ + 62 = 88   ☐ + 19 = 88

45 + ☐ = 88   39 + ☐ = 88

77 + ☐ = 88   ☐ + 1 = 88

Counting crossword

Work out the sums then write the numbers in words to
complete the crossword.

Across

1. 1 + 1 + 3 = ☐

2. 9 + 2 + 5 = ☐

3. 2 + 5 + 3 = ☐

4. 4 + 4 + 1 = ☐

Down

1. 2 + 1 + 1 = ☐

2. 3 + 4 + 1 = ☐

3. 7 + 1 + 3 = ☐

4. 2 + 2 + 3 = ☐

5. 5 + 4 + 3 = ☐

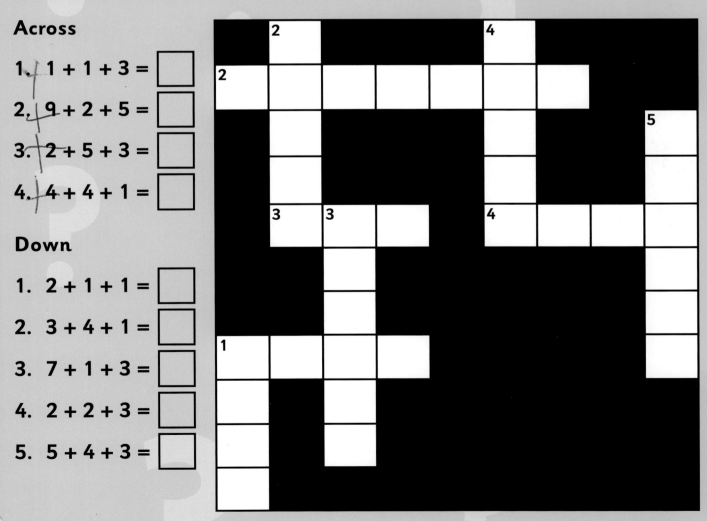

Answers

Pages 2-3
Count the candles
5 candles
2 candles
7 candles

10 candles
There are 14 children at
your party.

Fun with one
8 party hats
3 sandwiches
4 balls
6 jellies

Pages 4-5
Two for tea
9 strawberries
5 onions
4 loaves
8 oranges

Plus 2 practice
2 + 7 = 9
6 + 2 = 8
8 + 2 = 10

Some more sums
9 + 2 = 11
4 + 2 = 6
2 + 5 = 7

Zero zone
1 + 0 = 1
4 + 0 = 4
6 + 0 = 6

Pages 6-7
Ten pin teaser
3 + 5 = 8
4 + 2 = 6
2 + 5 = 7
8 + 1 = 9

The girl needs to knock down
5 pins with her second throw
to score a perfect 10.

Spot the spots
4 + 5 = 9
3 + 5 = 8
6 + 6 = 12
2 + 3 = 5
5 + 6 = 11

Pages 8-9
Animal antics
2 + 3 = 5 mice
5 + 4 = 9 giraffes
4 + 8 = 12 spiders
6 + 4 = 10 seagulls
3 + 2 = 5 animals

Nibbling numbers
number 9 fish
number 15 fish
number 11 fish

Pages 10-11
Up and down the line
16 + 5 = 21
8 + 8 = 16
14 + 5 = 19
3 + 9 = 12
4 + 4 = 8
13 + 7 = 20

Train-track maths
9 + 4 = 13
10 + 8 = 18
2 + 13 = 15
15 + 4 = 19

Pages 12-13
Perfect pairs
4 + 6 = 10
7 + 3 = 10
6 + 4 = 10
5 + 5 = 10

Pages 14-15
Top toys
20 + 7 + 3 = 30
6 + 3 + 3 = 12
2 + 3 + 4 = 9

Jungle hide and seek
5 + 10 + 12 = 27
7 + 7 + 7 + 8 = 29
1 + 3 + 4 + 1 = 9
9 + 11 + 3 = 23
10 + 13 + 17 = 40
3 + 4 + 2 + 6 = 15

Pages 16-17
Cloud cover
15 + 25 = 40
10 + 9 = 19
8 + 4 = 12
4 + 25 = 29
14 + 22 = 36
13 + 13 = 26

Daft doublers
6 + 6 = 12
7 + 7 = 14

Pages 18-19
Message in a bottle
53 days
24 days
3 ships
15 animals

Pages 20-21
Market day
26 HORSES 12 + 14 = 26
38 GEESE 16 + 22 = 38
55 CHICKENS 22 + 33 = 55
47 COWS 6 + 41 = 47
25 PIGS 11 + 14 = 25

Counting sheep
12 + 19 = 31 lambs
28 + 14 = 42 ewes
15 + 27 = 42 rams

Pages 22-23
Plus is no fuss
35 + 7 = 42
26 + 24 = 50
19 + 17 = 36
34 + 12 = 46

Number grids
There are several right
answers. Ask a friend or a
grown-up to check yours!

Pages 24-25
Food festival!
apple 10p + 5p
pizza 50p + 5p
juice 10p + 5p + 2p + 1p
spaghetti £1 + £1 + 20p +
20p + 5p
potato 50p + 20p + 2p + 2p

Pages 28-29
Chocolate challenge
$15 + 4 = 19$ chunks
of chocolate
$12 + 4 = 16$ chunks
of chocolate
$16 + 15 = 31$ chunks
of chocolate

Pirate problems
10 sails
12 cannons
18 gold coins

Eight is great
$14 + 74 = 88$
$26 + 62 = 88$
$45 + 43 = 88$
$77 + 11 = 88$
$53 + 35 = 88$
$69 + 19 = 88$
$39 + 49 = 88$
$87 + 1 = 88$

Counting crossword
Clues across:
1. $1 + 1 + 3 = 5$ f i v e
2. $9 + 2 + 5 = 16$ s i x t e e n
3. $2 + 5 + 3 = 10$ t e n
4. $4 + 4 + 1 = 9$ n i n e

Clues down:
1. $2 + 1 + 1 = 4$ f o u r
2. $3 + 4 + 1 = 8$ e i g h t
3. $7 + 1 + 3 = 11$ e l e v e n
4. $2 + 2 + 3 = 7$ s e v e n
5. $5 + 4 + 3 = 12$ t w e l v e

Reward chart

Use this chart to keep a record of your progress. Give yourself a sticker star when you see 'Sticker star time!' on the page.

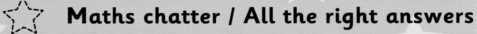

- ☆ **Party puzzlers**
- ☆ **Sums at the shops**
- ☆ **To ten and beyond**
- ☆ **Maths chatter / All the right answers**
- ☆ **Up and down the line**
- ☆ **Playing with numbers**
- ☆ **Swap shop / Adding more and more**
- ☆ **The sky's the limit!**
- ☆ **Challenging times**
- ☆ **Bigger and bigger!**
- ☆ **Plus is no fuss**
- ☆ **Funny money**

Sticker star time!